CRAZY CAT WOULD YOU RATHERS? FOR KIDS WHO LOVE CATS:

Funny Critters Cat Books for Kids

Crazy Cat Would You Rathers? For Kids Who Love Cats:

250+ Silly and Smart Would You Rathers? for Clever Kids– A Game Book Full of Hilarious, Interactive, and Challenging Questions, And a Funny Cat Book for Kids (8-12)

--By Funny Critters Cat Books for Kids--

Copyright © 2022 -

CONTENTS

SPECIAL BONUS!

Want This Bonus Book for free?

Get FREE, unlimited access to it and all of my new books by joining our Fan club!

SCAN W/ YOUR CAMERA TO JOIN!

1

DEAR PARENTS

One of the best ways for kids to learn more about themselves and the world around them is to ask questions. This book of cat-themed Would You Rathers? is a great way for kids to expand their imaginations and practice decision-making. And, it'll make them laugh a lot!!!

Written in a unique "Would You Rather" game format, these questions can be asked from kid to kid, parent to kid, or vice-versa! With a variety of topics ranging from school subjects and travel to pop culture and their love of cats, kids can have fun and connect with others at the same time. There is no better way to make a friendship stronger than to ask questions about what each of you would rather do…

We guarantee this book will offer lots of clean, wholesome, family-friendly fun for cat lovers of all ages.

--The Team at Funny Critters Cat Books for Kids

2

HEY, KIDS!

What do you like most about spending time with your kitty cat? Snuggling up to their soft fur, or watching them chase a toy around the room? Do they like to eat crunchy treats out of your hand or munch on a big stinky can of tuna fish?

This book is all about learning more about your best, furry friends– cats! If you think you know your cat really well, just wait until you read some of these questions. Do you know what your kitty would want to do if they went to school with you? Or how about if they had superpowers..?

Play this game with your friends or family and learn what they would rather do. See who can choose the best answers and make everybody else laugh the hardest!

3

HOW TO PLAY

———•◦◇◦•———

You can read this book by yourself. Or this book can be used as a game that can be played with 2 or more people.

Keep a score card to award those who choose the winning answer: the funniest, silliest, smartest, or most interesting answer! It's up to you to choose!

You can set a timer after each question to create a "thinking time." This will add some competitive pressure for players to really get their thinking caps on! The shorter the time, the higher the pressure – and the greater the excitement.

Using a visual timer such as an hourglass will add an extra buzz to the game as players watch the seconds run out…

Feel free to jump around through the sections or play them through one at a time. You choose how long to keep the fun going!

Have a great game!

4

AROUND THE HOUSE

Cats love to spend time at home, and when you come back from school, they are always there to greet you. So, we thought it would be interesting to ask some questions about what you and your furry friend would like to do (or not like to do) around the house…

Would your cat rather…?

1. Take a catnap with you or chase a toy around the kitchen?

2. Have bird feeders outside the window or an aquarium full of fish?

3. Lounge in the sun on a blanket outside or slide around a slippery floor?

4. Sleep on crinkly newspaper or a big and fluffy bean bag?

5. Have their own room in the house or share a bunk bed with you?

6. Lay outside and watch the clouds move or watch squirrels in a tree?

7. Press their paw on a computer keyboard or on piano keys?

8. Listen to birds singing or music?

9. Claw on corrugated cardboard or on the sofa cushions?

10. Have you brush their teeth or trim their claws?

11. Sit on a pillow on a warm, sunny windowsill or relax in the cool darkness under the bed?

12. Build a DIY cat tower or a cat tent?

13. Have cat bunk beds or a mini, cat-sized sofa?

14. Have a ground-level doorbell they could push at your front door or an automatically opening cat flap?

15. Nap on the countertop or the coffee table?

16. Drink water from a tap or from a bowl?

17. Put up with the noise of a leaf blower or a vacuum cleaner?

18. Hear the sound of a can opening or you calling them to come cuddle?

19. Watch the Animal Planet channel or cartoons?

20. Jump onto the kitchen counter or look out the window?

21. Explore the backyard or curl up in a pile of clothes?

22. Wake you up early to have breakfast together or sneak into the kitchen while everyone's asleep for a midnight snack?

23. Wake you up by jumping on your bed or by meowing louder than an alarm clock?

24. Play with one favorite toy all the time or play with a new toy every day?

25. Lick fresh water dripping from the sink or steal water from your cup?

26. Break into a bag of kitty kibble or steal food off your plate when you're not looking?

27. Rub against your leg when they want you to pet them or put their paws on you to get your attention?

28. Eat food straight from the can or have their food presented neatly on a nice fancy plate?

29. Play with another pet or get lots of cuddles from their favorite person?

30. Steal things from your room to play with or go hunting for bugs around the house?

31. Run up to every new person who visits the house or find a hidden hiding spot to watch strangers without being seen?

32. Watch cars driving by outside or climb a tree?

33. Chase their own tail or play with a bouncy ball?

34. Sleep all day long or stay up all night meowing?

35. Stay close to your side during a thunderstorm or run around in the rain?

36. Play with a new kitty or be the only pet in the house?

37. Take a warm bubble bath or clean themselves with their tongue?

5

FUN TIMES WITH THE KITTIES

Everybody has a different idea of what's fun or what's not. As you know, cats tend to have strong likes and dislikes... So why don't you tell us about what your cat thinks is fun and what it thinks is most def-fur-nately not!!

1. Learn how to give a high-five or how to fetch?

2. Swat at feathers on a string or tug on a ribbon?

3. Play with wrapping paper or toilet paper rolls?

4. Dodge around a ping-pong ball or follow a laser dot?

5. Play with a wind-up mouse or swat at a mini-drone that looks like a bird?

6. Play in a box full of packing peanuts or an empty box?

7. Play with a robotic fish or a hologram mouse?

8. Run on a hamster wheel or bounce on a trampoline?

9. Pounce on paper bags or explore empty cardboard boxes?

10. Get a birdwatching station or a cat tree?

11. Chase a ball at a baseball game or jump over obstacles on a running track?

12. Lounge on a floaty chair in the swimming pool or jump through a basketball hoop?

13. Slide down the lanes at a bowling alley or pounce on the whack-a-moles at the arcade?

14. Snuggle inside your sweater as you go ice skating or sit on your lap as you play bumper cars?

15. Ride a Ferris wheel to the top or play hide and seek under the blankets?

16. Perform gymnastics at the Olympics or compete in a hot dog eating contest?

17. Fly a kite attached to their tail or jump on a giant trampoline?

18. Nibble on wheatgrass or catnip?

19. Chase catnip-flavored bubbles or turkey-flavored ones?

20. Play with a bottle cap or a video game?

21. Run through a tunnel made of crinkly paper or lay in a hammock under the sun?

22. Hunt a toy mouse or real live fireflies?

23. Play with a giant ball of yarn or a 100-foot-long piece of string?

24. Find their way out of a maze or climb the curtains in the living room?

25. Swim in a pool of milk or climb a mountain covered in bubble wrap?

26. Play glow-in-the-dark laser tag or chase the ball on a mini-golf course?

27. Play with seagulls on the beach or watch cat videos on YouTube?

28. Defend a treehouse fort from squirrels or finger-paint with their paws?

29. Run along the bases at a baseball field or catch frisbees with you?

30. Be held in your arms while you go on a carousel or follow you down a slide?

31. Chase a bouncing tennis ball or paw at shiny marbles?

32. Snap at flies or knock over a tower of building blocks?

33. Take silly selfies with you or play twister with some other cats?

34. Swim through a bathtub full of cat toys or dive into a bowl of water?

6

CATS, SCHOOL, AND HOMEWORK

Imagine what would happen if you could take your cat to school with you. Wouldn't that be amazing? What would they rather do?

If your cat went to school with you, would they rather…?

1. Get lots of attention from all the students or stay in a closet where nobody could see them?

2. Run a mile around the track or play dodgeball in gym class?

3. Sleep underneath the teacher's desk or take a nap on a book in the library?

4. Solve math problems about how much kibble was in their bowl or learn how to meow in Spanish?

5. Search for a toy in the lost & found box or help the hall monitor keep a lookout for troublemakers?

6. Tell the teacher the dog ate their homework or sneak out the school window when the teacher isn't looking?

7. Play hide-and-seek at recess or swing on the swing set?

8. Eat the mystery meal for lunch in the cafeteria or be in a "cuddling booth" at the school fair?

9. Be the teacher's pet or spend time out in detention?

10. Build a cat tower in woodshop class or make a tuna fish casserole in cooking class?

11. Observe birds on the playground or beg the teacher for treats?

12. Enter the school talent show with their musical meows or study scientific facts about cats?

13. Watch a school football game or dig up flowers in the school garden?

14. Chase paper clips you throw at them or scratch the legs of your desk?

15. Purr to encourage the hard-working kids or hiss at the kids who are goofing off?

16. Meow in the school choir or walk all over the keyboard in computer class?

17. Sit on the rug during story time or show off their favorite toy during show-and-tell?

18. Sit at a regular desk and chair or lounge on a bookshelf in the classroom?

19. Patiently swish their tail waiting to be called on in class or meow loudly until the teacher picks them?

20. Watch you complete a school project or keep the teachers company while they grade student papers?

21. Be a mascot for the football team or play a miniature cat guitar in the school band?

7

WHEN KITTY GRADUATES…!

Maybe one day you'll become world-famous as an inventor or an astronaut. We all know that cats are too lazy to work, but if they did, what kinds of jobs would they rather?

Once your kitty graduates, would they rather…?

1. Design cat doors in a factory or stop bad kitties misbehaving by becoming a feline police officer?

2. Work remotely so they can make everyone laugh on video calls or go to the office and lie on a photocopier and get petted all the time?

3. Live in an alley with garbage cans in the big city or live in a barn in the country?

4. Test out armchairs for comfort in a furniture store or sample cat treats for a pet store?

5. Be a kitty therapist and purr on people's laps when they're sad, or be a health inspector looking for rats in restaurants?

6. Star in a cat food commercial or be the first cat to walk on Mars?

8

PARTIES, PRESENTS, AND TREATS

Your cat loves treats as much as you do. But have you ever thought about what fun things your kitty likes more than others? Well, here's your chance to think about what your cat would rather...

1. A party with a special DJ and colorful lights or a snuggly sleepover under the blankets?

2. Hop inside the gift bags or roll around in the wrapping paper?

3. Wear a silly birthday hat or a superhero cape?

4. Meow "Happy Birthday" by themselves, or have you sing "Happy Birthday" to them?

5. Be the center of attention at a party or take all the gifts and hide under the bed?

6. A party with balloon animals or a sleepover with freshly baked cat treats?

7. A shiny, sparkly toy or a very loud and noisy toy?

8. A crunchy treat to bite into or a very stinky can of fish?

9. A laser pointer to chase or a teddy bear to snuggle up to?

10. A shoe to chew on or a ball pit to play in?

11. A fuzzy mouse to hold in their mouth or a chance to knock something off the table?

12. Some catnip or a triple scoop tuna salad "ice cream cone?"

13. Cool sunglasses to block the light from their eyes or goggles so they can see underwater?

14. A present of a comfy new cat bed or a leash so you can take them out on walks?

15. Binoculars to spy on their cat neighbors or their own automatic can opener so they don't have to wait for you to feed them?

16. A knitted sweater with mouse designs on it or a little backpack to carry around their cat toys?

17. A toy bird that chirps or a toy mouse that runs around really fast?

18. Socks to keep their paws warm or a hat to keep their ears warm?

19. A toy that dangles from a string or one that can fly around in the air?

20. A giant crab cake with gravy frosting or ice cream with anchovies and chicken on top

21. Stay up all night to party or take a nap during their own party?

22. Play with confetti paper or swat at party balloons?

23. Be gifted a new toy by you or play laser tag for twenty minutes?

9

YOUR CAT AND OTHER ANIMALS

Cats aren't the only interesting animals. Most of these other creatures might not be suitable friends for your kitty. However, it's fun to imagine what fun and games they and your cat might get up to. So let your imagination go wild...

1. Swing in the trees with monkeys or take a nap with a sloth?

2. Howl with a pack of wolves, or go hunting with lions?

3. Hop around in a kangaroo's pouch, or sit up high on a giraffe's back?

4. Spin a web with a spider, or play in a butterfly garden?

5. Be friends with a platypus or try to catch a flying fish?

6. Eat ants with an anteater or eat tuna fresh from the sea?

7. Hoot at night with an owl, or crow in the morning with a rooster?

8. Be camouflaged in the leaves like an iguana, or tunnel underground like a groundhog?

9. Giggle with hyenas or grow striped fur like zebras?

10. Herd sheep on a farm like a sheepdog or hee-haw like a donkey?

11. Lay eggs like a chicken, or roll in the mud like a pig?

12. Get sprayed with water from an elephant's trunk, or go surfing with dolphins?

13. Ride on a horse's back or help a chicken sit on her eggs?

14. Help a squirrel gather nuts or hang upside down with bats?

Would you rather…?

1. A cat that was polka-dotted like a ladybug or had a lot of legs like a caterpillar?

2. Your cat had a shell like a turtle or webbed feet like a duck?

3. Your cat snorted like a pig when they sleep or chirped like a bird when they woke you up?

4. Your cat liked to be walked on a leash like a dog or could waddle like a duck?

5. Your cat could slither like a snake or hop around like a bunny

6. Your cat had spikes like a porcupine, or they could spray like a skunk?

7. Your cat could grow a mane like a lion or tail feathers like a peacock?

8. Be able to ride your cat like a horse or have a cat as small as a mouse?

9. Your cat walked sideways like a crab or they wiggled around like a worm?

10. Your cat was as big as a bear or had a pouch on their belly like a wallaby?

11. Your cat had lots of teeth like a crocodile or your cat could stand on one leg like a flamingo?

12. Your cat could swim like a dolphin or flop around on their belly like a seal?

10

CREATIVE KITTIES

Music, art, and other creative past times make our lives more fun and interesting. What if your kitty could join in and be creative with you?

1. Have a portrait painted of them like the Mona Lisa or a gold statue of them in front of the house

2. Pluck strings on a guitar or on a harp?

3. Play the accordion or break dance?

4. Do stunts in a movie or be a mascot for a sports team?

5. Walk across a piano keyboard or pluck at guitar strings?

6. Play with kitty hand puppets or bake cat-shaped cookies?

7. Use their paws to make clay pottery or be part of a dancing flash mob?

Would you rather...

1. Your cat played the flute or could sing like Lady Gaga?

2. Make a tiny hat for your cat or a cat hoodie sweatshirt?

3. Your cat could appear with you in a YouTube video or do a comedy act on stage in a theater?

4. Had a cat who could tap-dance or play a miniature cat banjo?

5. Dance to salsa music with your kitty or make colorful jewelry for your cat?

6. Make a rap song with your cat or start a rock band together?

7. See the musical "Cats" with your kitty or become a cat dance instructor?

8. Bake a cake that looks like your cat or make a 3D printout of your cat?

9. Write a book about cats or become your cat's agent for pet food commercials?

10. Make a music video with your cat or become street performers together?

11. Write a song about your kitty or draw a comic book about cats?

12. Dance with a crew of cats or sing your kitty to sleep at night

13. Direct a movie with your cat or dress up in a cat costume and surprise your kitty?

14. Listen to cats singing or write a poem about cats?

15. Crack jokes as a comedy duo with your cat or design a cat-shaped house?

11

CAT SUPERPOWERS

Have you ever wondered if your cat had amazing talents or even superpowers? Life would be awesome, don't you agree? Read on, and let's explore the possibilities…

If your cat could have a superpower, would you rather...?

1. They could sneak around like a ninja or fall from really tall places and be okay?

2. They could charge your phone with static electricity from their fur or they could jump around like a goat?

3. They could meow a song or clap their paws when you sing?

4. They had super speed or the power of invisibility?

5. They could stretch their arms out really long or move objects with their mind?

6. They could fly or they could talk?

7. They could control the weather or they could grow flowers wherever they walk?

8. They could time travel to any time period, or teleport to any location?

9. They were half mermaid or half dinosaur?

10. They had mind-control or could transform into an umbrella when it rains?

11. Their tummy could turn into a tv screen or they could play music out of their mouths?

12. They could communicate with you telepathically or they could get you out of trouble with your parents?

13. They could warm you up you like a scarf or coat when it's cold or cool you down when it's really hot?

14. Their bodies could shine like a light when it's dark or they could block out the sun to make it nighttime whenever you wanted?

15. They could pick you up with their tail or they could bounce you around like a ball?

16. They could spit fire like a dragon, or they could create multiple cat clones of themselves?

17. They could answer any question you have or grant any wish you have?

18. They could freeze time or they could transform into any animal?

19. They could stick to anything like glue or candy could come out of their ears?

20. They could change their voice to sound like any person you want, or they could sing people to sleep?

21. Any room they walk into would become clean or they could heal anyone?

22. They could grant three wishes like a genie, or they could fly through the sky?

23. They could find anything you misplace or help you make friends with anyone?

24. They could be very persuasive with your parents or they could do anything you could do?

25. Their fur was as long as Rapunzel's or they were hairless (but super strong)?

26. They could predict the future, or they could live forever?

27. Your kitty created a tornado every time they chased their own tail or created an earthquake when they jumped off the armchair?

12

AROUND THE WORLD WITH YOUR KITTY

What would it be like if you and your kitty could travel anywhere? What kinds of adventures would you have?

1. Eat sushi in Japan or fried liver in France?

2. Live in a tent in the desert in Morocco or in a tree house in a tropical jungle in Brazil?

3. Laugh with hyenas in Tanzania or explore the streets of New York City?

4. Go rafting down the Nile River or sunbathe with lemurs in Madagascar?

5. Walk along the Great Wall of China or perform cat acrobatics at the Super Bowl Half-Time Show?

6. Hang out with alpacas in Peru or waddle with penguins in Antarctica?

7. Help you build sandcastles on the beach in Puerto Rico or eat burgers in England?

8. Watch hula dancers in Hawaii, or watch skateboarders in Seattle?

9. Meet the presidents of countries or pop stars?

10. Smash a piñata for candy in Mexico or cuddle with koalas in Australia?

11. Go ice-fishing in Alaska or look for bears at Yellowstone National Park?

12. Ride on a moose's back in Canada or eat pepperoni pizza in Rome?

13. Chase a soccer ball in Spain or ride a boat on Lake Tahoe?

14. Race a cheetah in Tanzania, or race a road runner in Arizona?

15. Meet elephants in Thailand or slide down glaciers in Iceland?

16. Gaze at the Northern Lights in Norway or lounge by the waterfalls in Hawaii?

17. Eat spring rolls in Vietnam or visit a castle in Poland full of mice?

18. Dress up like vampires in Transylvania or leprechauns in Ireland?

19. Dance to reggae music in Jamaica or smell stinky snails in France?

20. Chase butterflies in California or lie in the sun on a Caribbean island?

21. Sniff catnip in Germany or sample smoked salmon in Norway?

22. Eat sausages in Poland or nibble on anchovies in Italy?

23. Take selfies with their lion cousins in Kenya or explore a spooky Hungarian castle full of mice?

13

HUGS AND CUDDLES

You love your cat, and your cat loves you. So, what are the best ways to show you care? What would your cat prefer you to do?

Would your cat rather...?

1. You brush their fur or tickle them under the chin?

2. Have their belly scratched with a bath sponge or get a back massage?

3. Lay in a field full of fresh catnip or have a pampered spa day?

4. Cuddle with twenty other cats or a hundred stuffed animals?

5. Have a pat on the head or their tummy tickled?

6. Get their head or their paws massaged?

7. Lick your face or give you a friendly head-butt?

8. Have their nose scratched or be carried in your arms around the house?

9. Make biscuits on your tummy or nuzzle their head against you?

10. Snuggle on your lap or be draped across your shoulder and purr in your ear?

11. Follow you around all day or be carried in your backpack?

12. Fall asleep with you every night or wake you up by licking your face every morning?

14

KINDA' RANDOM

Sometimes it's fun to think about situations that are really crazy and fantastical. So, these scenarios should really make you think and definitely make you laugh…

1. Win an unlimited supply of scratching posts or help create a brand-new cat food flavor?

2. Roll around in a giant hamster wheel or have a cat toy made out of a hundred jingle bells

3. Sneak around the house and jump out to surprise you or be carried in your arms everywhere you go?

4. Stretch out on the floor or curl up in a warm spot?

5. Glide down a slide or play on a seesaw?

6. Chase after a fast lizard or watch a ladybug crawling on a leaf?

7. Live at the top of a tall tower or in an underground cave?

8. Be dressed up like a caveman or dressed up like a dinosaur?

9. Have a secret hiding spot underneath the floorboards or a hole in an enormous tree trunk?

10. Be able to fly with birds or swim with fish?

11. Be able to disappear and reappear whenever they want or have the ability to walk through walls?

12. Go a day without eating or spend a night sleeping outside in the cold?

13. Visit a friendly vet or sit in a corner for one hour?

14. Eat slimy snails or try to steal a nut from a squirrel?

15. Eat a steak from a gold plate or eat a cheeseburger out of the trash?

16. Be able to fit into small spaces or be able to stretch out to the size of an entire couch?

17. Go an entire day without anyone able to see them or go one hour without anyone able to pet them?

18. Eat a cockroach or slurp up an entire eel?

19. Have an itch they can't scratch or cough up a horrible hairball?

20. Be able to smell you from a mile away or be able to see tiny bugs all the way over on the neighbor's lawn?

21. Lose the ability to see but gain super speed or lose the ability to walk but gain the ability to fly?

22. Be trapped in a room with a hundred cockroaches or be surrounded by twenty rats?

23. Become a white tiger living in the snow or become a lion that is the king of the animals?

24. Play on a jungle gym with other cats or spend the day at a cat spa being pampered?

Would you rather...?

1. Your kitty gobbled up food like a black hole or that anything your kitty steals from your room ended up in a different dimension?

2. Your cat had long teeth like a saber-toothed tiger or scales like an alligator?

3. Your cat could roar like a lion or could squeak like a mouse?

4. Your cat wore a collar with 50 jingle bells on it or socks that lit up when they walked?

5. Have a cat whose fur was plaid or a cat whose fur was like a rainbow?

6. Your cat had a horn like a unicorn or opposable thumbs like a monkey?

7. Your cat smelled like rotten eggs or was slimy like a fish?

8. Your cat left footprints everywhere they walked or you could hear their meow from miles away?

9. Your cat turned into a spider once a month or smelled like a skunk once a week?

10. Your cat's fur turned red every time they were mad or their eyes turned purple every time they were hungry?

11. Have twenty cats laying on you all night or one very fat cat that you would have to carry all the way to the store and back?

12. Your cat demanded to be hand-fed a sardine every night or you had to share a slice of anchovy pizza with your cat every day?

13. Your cat's ears were as long as a bunny's, or your cat's tail was small and round like a cotton ball?

14. Your cat's whiskers could move around like antennas, or their claws could grow to be an inch long?

15

THAT'S ALL "FUR" NOW!

·••◇••·

Wow, you made it to the end of the book. That's PAW-some! How many new things did you learn about yourself and your furry friend?

Do you have some ideas on cool toys and gifts you could spoil your kitty with? Or maybe an exciting adventure the two of you could do the next time you're having fun together!

Whenever you're down or bored, come back to this book and remember everything that you could do with your cat. Surely, you'll get a few laughs and giggles out of it!

Who knows, you might even come up with some questions yourself...?

So, what do you think you'd rather do with your kitty now?

Did You Like This Book?

Why don't you leave a review???

Follow the link or QR code below. There you can leave it as many stars as you like!

Thanks!

Follow this link to review
https://www.amazon.com/review/create-review/?ie=UTF8&channel=glance-detail&asin=1736763059

Or, simply scan this QR code...

Purrr-leeze leave a review!
Show that you like crazy cats!!!

Want to Read Other Funny Cat Books?

How about starting with this one….?

SPECIAL BONUS!

Want This Bonus Book for free?

Get FREE, unlimited access to it and all of my new books by joining our Fan club!

SCAN W/ YOUR CAMERA TO JOIN!

DISCLAIMER

This information is for entertainment purposes only.

The information provided herein is stated to be truthful and consistent, in that any liability, in terms of inattention or otherwise, by any usage or abuse of any policies, processes, or directions contained within is the solitary and utter responsibility of the recipient reader. Under no circumstances will any legal responsibility or blame be held against the publisher for any reparation, damages, or monetary loss due to the information herein, either directly or indirectly.

Made in the USA
Columbia, SC
17 December 2023

28767103R00045